Quieting Your Heart

6-MONTH BIBLE-STUDY JOURNAL

DARLENE SCHACHT, THE TIME-WARP WIFE

Peace

Be Strong and Courageous

Quieting Your Heart: 6-Month Bible-Study Journal

Time-Warp Wife
Suite 5-1377 Border Street
Winnipeg, Manitoba
R3H 0N1

Copyright © 2016 by Darlene Schacht

Cover design by Darlene Schacht

ISBN 978-0-9950567-0-1

Images from Bigstock.com

Find Darlene Schacht on the web here:
Blog: TimeWarpWife.com
Facebook: timewarpwife
Twitter: timewarpwife
Pinterest: timewarpwife

Two Ways to Study

SCRATCHING THE SURFACE

Choose a portion of scripture to read, either on a certain topic or make your way through a book of the Bible. You can find free Bible study guides at www.timewarpwife.com.

Ask yourself these kinds of questions:

- What is the main concept, or what is God telling me here?

- How can I apply this to my life?

- Is there sin I need to examine?

DIGGING DEEP INTO THE WORD

Take a step deeper and dig into the Word.

Here are a few ways to do that:

- Look up the scripture in a commentary like Matthew Henry's or grab a different translation, and read it again. Is there anything that you missed the first time?

- Research the characters online. What else can you learn about them?

- Cross reference key verses that stand out to you. You can cross reference any verse online at: http://www.openbible.info/labs/cross-references/

- Look for life application principles. Ask yourself how you can improve in this area.

- Use the Blue Letter Bible at http://www.blueletterbible.org where you'll find interlinear Greek and Hebrew translations, as well as other awesome Bible study tools.

1/2020

TODAY I'M READING
1 Tim 4

Peace Filled

GOD IS...
Awesome
Merceful
loving
kindness

3 THINGS I'M THANKFUL FOR
Holy spirit   Jesus
God my father

V14

THIS IS WHAT I LEARNED TODAY
Be Secure in who I am & whose I am
who you made me to be. How
you made me and the contribution
you have made for me to be. give
Watch your life Because it
is BEING Watched.
More than a conqueror. Victorious
Understand Some will choose deception.
Set your example in speech life
love faith & purity. Dont neglect your gift.
Be diligent. Give yourself wholly

TODAY. I'M READING

GOD IS...

3 THINGS I'M THANKFUL FOR

THIS IS WHAT I LEARNED TODAY

TODAY I'M READING

GOD IS...

3 THINGS I'M THANKFUL FOR

THIS IS WHAT I LEARNED TODAY

TODAY I'M READING

GOD IS...

3 THINGS I'M THANKFUL FOR

THIS IS WHAT I LEARNED TODAY

TODAY I'M READING

GOD IS...

3 THINGS I'M THANKFUL FOR

THIS IS WHAT I LEARNED TODAY

TODAY I'M READING

GOD IS...

3 THINGS I'M THANKFUL FOR

THIS IS WHAT I LEARNED TODAY

TODAY I'M READING

GOD IS...

3 THINGS I'M THANKFUL FOR

THIS IS WHAT I LEARNED TODAY

TODAY I'M READING

GOD IS...

3 THINGS I'M THANKFUL FOR

THIS IS WHAT I LEARNED TODAY

TODAY I'M READING

GOD IS...

3 THINGS I'M THANKFUL FOR

THIS IS WHAT I LEARNED TODAY

TODAY I'M READING

GOD IS...

3 THINGS I'M THANKFUL FOR

THIS IS WHAT I LEARNED TODAY

TODAY I'M READING

GOD IS...

3 THINGS I'M THANKFUL FOR

THIS IS WHAT I LEARNED TODAY

TODAY I'M READING

GOD IS...

3 THINGS I'M THANKFUL FOR

THIS IS WHAT I LEARNED TODAY

TODAY I'M READING

GOD IS...

3 THINGS I'M THANKFUL FOR

THIS IS WHAT I LEARNED TODAY

TODAY I'M READING

GOD IS...

3 THINGS I'M THANKFUL FOR

THIS IS WHAT I LEARNED TODAY

TODAY I'M READING

GOD IS...

3 THINGS I'M THANKFUL FOR

THIS IS WHAT I LEARNED TODAY

TODAY I'M READING

GOD IS...

3 THINGS I'M THANKFUL FOR

THIS IS WHAT I LEARNED TODAY

TODAY I'M READING

GOD IS...

3 THINGS I'M THANKFUL FOR

THIS IS WHAT I LEARNED TODAY

TODAY I'M READING

GOD IS...

3 THINGS I'M THANKFUL FOR

THIS IS WHAT I LEARNED TODAY

TODAY I'M READING

GOD IS...

3 THINGS I'M THANKFUL FOR

THIS IS WHAT I LEARNED TODAY

TODAY I'M READING

GOD IS...

3 THINGS I'M THANKFUL FOR

THIS IS WHAT I LEARNED TODAY

TODAY I'M READING

GOD IS...

3 THINGS I'M THANKFUL FOR

THIS IS WHAT I LEARNED TODAY

TODAY I'M READING

GOD IS...

3 THINGS I'M THANKFUL FOR

THIS IS WHAT I LEARNED TODAY

TODAY I'M READING

GOD IS...

3 THINGS I'M THANKFUL FOR

THIS IS WHAT I LEARNED TODAY

TODAY I'M READING

GOD IS...

3 THINGS I'M THANKFUL FOR

THIS IS WHAT I LEARNED TODAY

TODAY I'M READING

GOD IS...

3 THINGS I'M THANKFUL FOR

THIS IS WHAT I LEARNED TODAY

TODAY I'M READING

GOD IS...

3 THINGS I'M THANKFUL FOR

THIS IS WHAT I LEARNED TODAY

TODAY I'M READING

GOD IS...

3 THINGS I'M THANKFUL FOR

THIS IS WHAT I LEARNED TODAY

TODAY I'M READING

GOD IS...

3 THINGS I'M THANKFUL FOR

THIS IS WHAT I LEARNED TODAY

TODAY I'M READING

GOD IS...

3 THINGS I'M THANKFUL FOR

THIS IS WHAT I LEARNED TODAY

TODAY I'M READING

GOD IS...

3 THINGS I'M THANKFUL FOR

THIS IS WHAT I LEARNED TODAY

TODAY I'M READING

GOD IS...

3 THINGS I'M THANKFUL FOR

THIS IS WHAT I LEARNED TODAY

TODAY I'M READING

GOD IS...

3 THINGS I'M THANKFUL FOR

THIS IS WHAT I LEARNED TODAY

TODAY I'M READING

GOD IS...

3 THINGS I'M THANKFUL FOR

THIS IS WHAT I LEARNED TODAY

TODAY I'M READING

GOD IS...

3 THINGS I'M THANKFUL FOR

THIS IS WHAT I LEARNED TODAY

TODAY I'M READING

GOD IS...

3 THINGS I'M THANKFUL FOR

THIS IS WHAT I LEARNED TODAY

TODAY I'M READING

GOD IS...

3 THINGS I'M THANKFUL FOR

THIS IS WHAT I LEARNED TODAY

TODAY I'M READING

GOD IS...

3 THINGS I'M THANKFUL FOR

THIS IS WHAT I LEARNED TODAY

TODAY I'M READING

GOD IS...

3 THINGS I'M THANKFUL FOR

THIS IS WHAT I LEARNED TODAY

TODAY I'M READING

GOD IS...

3 THINGS I'M THANKFUL FOR

THIS IS WHAT I LEARNED TODAY

TODAY I'M READING

GOD IS...

3 THINGS I'M THANKFUL FOR

THIS IS WHAT I LEARNED TODAY

TODAY I'M READING

GOD IS...

3 THINGS I'M THANKFUL FOR

THIS IS WHAT I LEARNED TODAY

TODAY I'M READING

GOD IS...

3 THINGS I'M THANKFUL FOR

THIS IS WHAT I LEARNED TODAY

TODAY I'M READING

GOD IS...

3 THINGS I'M THANKFUL FOR

THIS IS WHAT I LEARNED TODAY

TODAY I'M READING

GOD IS...

3 THINGS I'M THANKFUL FOR

THIS IS WHAT I LEARNED TODAY

TODAY I'M READING

GOD IS...

3 THINGS I'M THANKFUL FOR

THIS IS WHAT I LEARNED TODAY

TODAY I'M READING

GOD IS...

3 THINGS I'M THANKFUL FOR

THIS IS WHAT I LEARNED TODAY

TODAY I'M READING

GOD IS...

3 THINGS I'M THANKFUL FOR

THIS IS WHAT I LEARNED TODAY

TODAY I'M READING

GOD IS...

3 THINGS I'M THANKFUL FOR

THIS IS WHAT I LEARNED TODAY

TODAY I'M READING

GOD IS...

3 THINGS I'M THANKFUL FOR

THIS IS WHAT I LEARNED TODAY

TODAY I'M READING

GOD IS...

3 THINGS I'M THANKFUL FOR

THIS IS WHAT I LEARNED TODAY

TODAY I'M READING

GOD IS...

3 THINGS I'M THANKFUL FOR

THIS IS WHAT I LEARNED TODAY

TODAY I'M READING

GOD IS...

3 THINGS I'M THANKFUL FOR

THIS IS WHAT I LEARNED TODAY

TODAY I'M READING

GOD IS...

3 THINGS I'M THANKFUL FOR

THIS IS WHAT I LEARNED TODAY

TODAY I'M READING

GOD IS...

3 THINGS I'M THANKFUL FOR

THIS IS WHAT I LEARNED TODAY

TODAY I'M READING

GOD IS...

3 THINGS I'M THANKFUL FOR

THIS IS WHAT I LEARNED TODAY

TODAY I'M READING

GOD IS...

3 THINGS I'M THANKFUL FOR

THIS IS WHAT I LEARNED TODAY

TODAY I'M READING

GOD IS...

3 THINGS I'M THANKFUL FOR

THIS IS WHAT I LEARNED TODAY

TODAY I'M READING

GOD IS...

3 THINGS I'M THANKFUL FOR

THIS IS WHAT I LEARNED TODAY

TODAY I'M READING

GOD IS...

3 THINGS I'M THANKFUL FOR

THIS IS WHAT I LEARNED TODAY

TODAY I'M READING

GOD IS...

3 THINGS I'M THANKFUL FOR

THIS IS WHAT I LEARNED TODAY

TODAY I'M READING

GOD IS...

3 THINGS I'M THANKFUL FOR

THIS IS WHAT I LEARNED TODAY

TODAY I'M READING

GOD IS...

3 THINGS I'M THANKFUL FOR

THIS IS WHAT I LEARNED TODAY

TODAY I'M READING

GOD IS...

3 THINGS I'M THANKFUL FOR

THIS IS WHAT I LEARNED TODAY

TODAY I'M READING

GOD IS...

3 THINGS I'M THANKFUL FOR

THIS IS WHAT I LEARNED TODAY

TODAY I'M READING

GOD IS...

3 THINGS I'M THANKFUL FOR

THIS IS WHAT I LEARNED TODAY

TODAY I'M READING

GOD IS...

3 THINGS I'M THANKFUL FOR

THIS IS WHAT I LEARNED TODAY

TODAY I'M READING

GOD IS...

3 THINGS I'M THANKFUL FOR

THIS IS WHAT I LEARNED TODAY

TODAY I'M READING

_____
_____
_____
_____

GOD IS...

_____
_____
_____
_____

3 THINGS I'M THANKFUL FOR

_____
_____
_____

THIS IS WHAT I LEARNED TODAY

_____
_____
_____
_____
_____
_____
_____
_____
_____
_____

TODAY I'M READING

GOD IS...

3 THINGS I'M THANKFUL FOR

THIS IS WHAT I LEARNED TODAY

TODAY I'M READING

GOD IS...

3 THINGS I'M THANKFUL FOR

THIS IS WHAT I LEARNED TODAY

TODAY I'M READING

_____
_____
_____
_____

GOD IS...

_____
_____
_____
_____

3 THINGS I'M THANKFUL FOR

_____
_____
_____

THIS IS WHAT I LEARNED TODAY

_____
_____
_____
_____
_____
_____
_____
_____
_____
_____

TODAY I'M READING

GOD IS...

3 THINGS I'M THANKFUL FOR

THIS IS WHAT I LEARNED TODAY

TODAY I'M READING

GOD IS...

3 THINGS I'M THANKFUL FOR

THIS IS WHAT I LEARNED TODAY

TODAY I'M READING

GOD IS...

3 THINGS I'M THANKFUL FOR

THIS IS WHAT I LEARNED TODAY

TODAY I'M READING

GOD IS...

3 THINGS I'M THANKFUL FOR

THIS IS WHAT I LEARNED TODAY

TODAY I'M READING

GOD IS...

3 THINGS I'M THANKFUL FOR

THIS IS WHAT I LEARNED TODAY

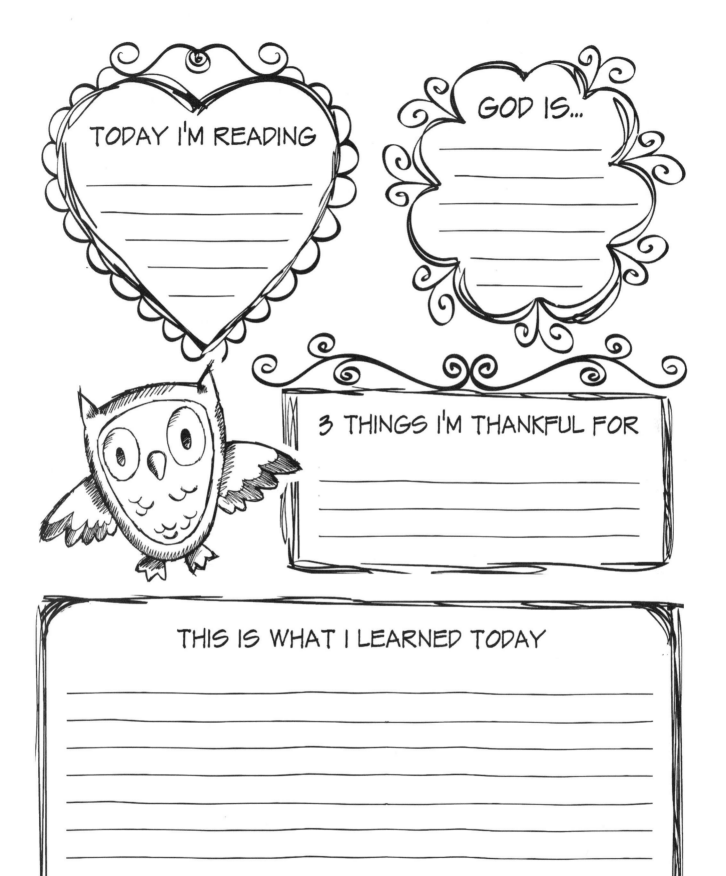

TODAY I'M READING

GOD IS...

3 THINGS I'M THANKFUL FOR

THIS IS WHAT I LEARNED TODAY

TODAY I'M READING

GOD IS...

3 THINGS I'M THANKFUL FOR

THIS IS WHAT I LEARNED TODAY

TODAY I'M READING

GOD IS...

3 THINGS I'M THANKFUL FOR

THIS IS WHAT I LEARNED TODAY

TODAY I'M READING

GOD IS...

3 THINGS I'M THANKFUL FOR

THIS IS WHAT I LEARNED TODAY

TODAY I'M READING

GOD IS...

3 THINGS I'M THANKFUL FOR

THIS IS WHAT I LEARNED TODAY

TODAY I'M READING

GOD IS...

3 THINGS I'M THANKFUL FOR

THIS IS WHAT I LEARNED TODAY

TODAY I'M READING

GOD IS...

3 THINGS I'M THANKFUL FOR

THIS IS WHAT I LEARNED TODAY

TODAY I'M READING

GOD IS...

3 THINGS I'M THANKFUL FOR

THIS IS WHAT I LEARNED TODAY

TODAY I'M READING

GOD IS...

3 THINGS I'M THANKFUL FOR

THIS IS WHAT I LEARNED TODAY

TODAY I'M READING

GOD IS...

3 THINGS I'M THANKFUL FOR

THIS IS WHAT I LEARNED TODAY

TODAY I'M READING

GOD IS...

3 THINGS I'M THANKFUL FOR

THIS IS WHAT I LEARNED TODAY

TODAY I'M READING

GOD IS...

3 THINGS I'M THANKFUL FOR

THIS IS WHAT I LEARNED TODAY

TODAY I'M READING

GOD IS...

3 THINGS I'M THANKFUL FOR

THIS IS WHAT I LEARNED TODAY

TODAY I'M READING

GOD IS...

3 THINGS I'M THANKFUL FOR

THIS IS WHAT I LEARNED TODAY

TODAY I'M READING

GOD IS...

3 THINGS I'M THANKFUL FOR

THIS IS WHAT I LEARNED TODAY

TODAY I'M READING

GOD IS...

3 THINGS I'M THANKFUL FOR

THIS IS WHAT I LEARNED TODAY

TODAY I'M READING

GOD IS...

3 THINGS I'M THANKFUL FOR

THIS IS WHAT I LEARNED TODAY

TODAY I'M READING

GOD IS...

3 THINGS I'M THANKFUL FOR

THIS IS WHAT I LEARNED TODAY

TODAY I'M READING

GOD IS...

3 THINGS I'M THANKFUL FOR

THIS IS WHAT I LEARNED TODAY

TODAY I'M READING

GOD IS...

3 THINGS I'M THANKFUL FOR

THIS IS WHAT I LEARNED TODAY

TODAY I'M READING

GOD IS...

3 THINGS I'M THANKFUL FOR

THIS IS WHAT I LEARNED TODAY

TODAY I'M READING

GOD IS...

3 THINGS I'M THANKFUL FOR

THIS IS WHAT I LEARNED TODAY

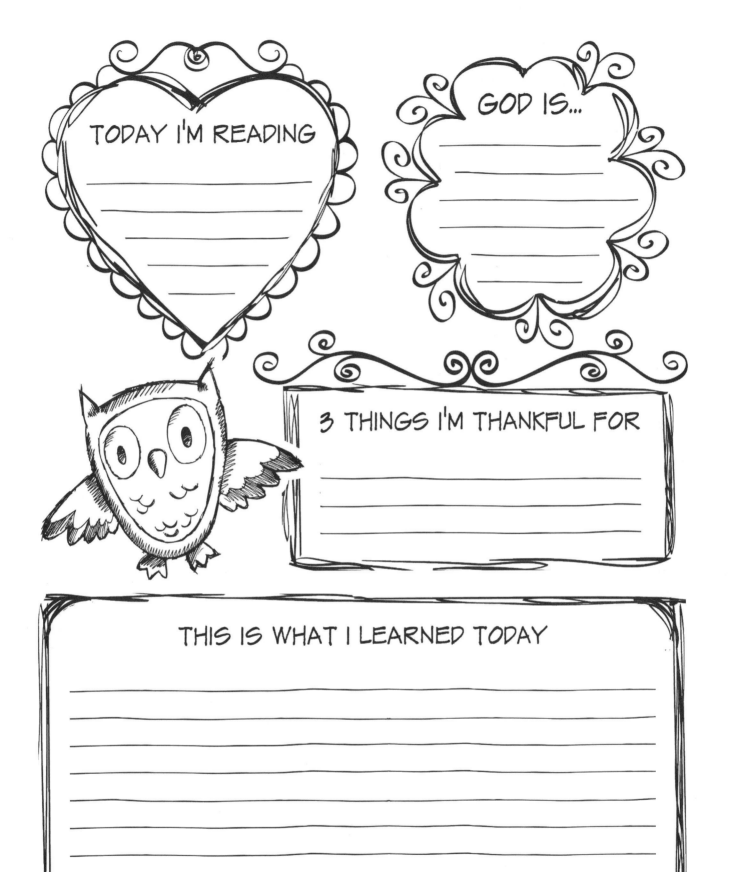

TODAY I'M READING

GOD IS...

3 THINGS I'M THANKFUL FOR

THIS IS WHAT I LEARNED TODAY

TODAY I'M READING

GOD IS...

3 THINGS I'M THANKFUL FOR

THIS IS WHAT I LEARNED TODAY

TODAY I'M READING

GOD IS...

3 THINGS I'M THANKFUL FOR

THIS IS WHAT I LEARNED TODAY

TODAY I'M READING

GOD IS...

3 THINGS I'M THANKFUL FOR

THIS IS WHAT I LEARNED TODAY

TODAY I'M READING

GOD IS...

3 THINGS I'M THANKFUL FOR

THIS IS WHAT I LEARNED TODAY

TODAY I'M READING

GOD IS...

3 THINGS I'M THANKFUL FOR

THIS IS WHAT I LEARNED TODAY

TODAY I'M READING

GOD IS...

3 THINGS I'M THANKFUL FOR

THIS IS WHAT I LEARNED TODAY

TODAY I'M READING

GOD IS...

3 THINGS I'M THANKFUL FOR

THIS IS WHAT I LEARNED TODAY

TODAY I'M READING

GOD IS...

3 THINGS I'M THANKFUL FOR

THIS IS WHAT I LEARNED TODAY

TODAY I'M READING

GOD IS...

3 THINGS I'M THANKFUL FOR

THIS IS WHAT I LEARNED TODAY

TODAY I'M READING

GOD IS...

3 THINGS I'M THANKFUL FOR

THIS IS WHAT I LEARNED TODAY

TODAY I'M READING

GOD IS...

3 THINGS I'M THANKFUL FOR

THIS IS WHAT I LEARNED TODAY

TODAY I'M READING

GOD IS...

3 THINGS I'M THANKFUL FOR

THIS IS WHAT I LEARNED TODAY

TODAY I'M READING

GOD IS...

3 THINGS I'M THANKFUL FOR

THIS IS WHAT I LEARNED TODAY

TODAY I'M READING

GOD IS...

3 THINGS I'M THANKFUL FOR

THIS IS WHAT I LEARNED TODAY

TODAY I'M READING

GOD IS...

3 THINGS I'M THANKFUL FOR

THIS IS WHAT I LEARNED TODAY

TODAY I'M READING

GOD IS...

3 THINGS I'M THANKFUL FOR

THIS IS WHAT I LEARNED TODAY

TODAY I'M READING

GOD IS...

3 THINGS I'M THANKFUL FOR

THIS IS WHAT I LEARNED TODAY

TODAY I'M READING

GOD IS...

3 THINGS I'M THANKFUL FOR

THIS IS WHAT I LEARNED TODAY

TODAY I'M READING

GOD IS...

3 THINGS I'M THANKFUL FOR

THIS IS WHAT I LEARNED TODAY

TODAY I'M READING

GOD IS...

3 THINGS I'M THANKFUL FOR

THIS IS WHAT I LEARNED TODAY

TODAY I'M READING

GOD IS...

3 THINGS I'M THANKFUL FOR

THIS IS WHAT I LEARNED TODAY

TODAY I'M READING

GOD IS...

3 THINGS I'M THANKFUL FOR

THIS IS WHAT I LEARNED TODAY

TODAY I'M READING

GOD IS...

3 THINGS I'M THANKFUL FOR

THIS IS WHAT I LEARNED TODAY

TODAY I'M READING

GOD IS...

3 THINGS I'M THANKFUL FOR

THIS IS WHAT I LEARNED TODAY

TODAY I'M READING

GOD IS...

3 THINGS I'M THANKFUL FOR

THIS IS WHAT I LEARNED TODAY

TODAY I'M READING

GOD IS...

3 THINGS I'M THANKFUL FOR

THIS IS WHAT I LEARNED TODAY

TODAY I'M READING

GOD IS...

3 THINGS I'M THANKFUL FOR

THIS IS WHAT I LEARNED TODAY

TODAY I'M READING

GOD IS...

3 THINGS I'M THANKFUL FOR

THIS IS WHAT I LEARNED TODAY

TODAY I'M READING

GOD IS...

3 THINGS I'M THANKFUL FOR

THIS IS WHAT I LEARNED TODAY

TODAY I'M READING

GOD IS...

3 THINGS I'M THANKFUL FOR

THIS IS WHAT I LEARNED TODAY

TODAY I'M READING

GOD IS...

3 THINGS I'M THANKFUL FOR

THIS IS WHAT I LEARNED TODAY

TODAY I'M READING

GOD IS...

3 THINGS I'M THANKFUL FOR

THIS IS WHAT I LEARNED TODAY

TODAY I'M READING

GOD IS...

3 THINGS I'M THANKFUL FOR

THIS IS WHAT I LEARNED TODAY

TODAY I'M READING

GOD IS...

3 THINGS I'M THANKFUL FOR

THIS IS WHAT I LEARNED TODAY

TODAY I'M READING

GOD IS...

3 THINGS I'M THANKFUL FOR

THIS IS WHAT I LEARNED TODAY

TODAY I'M READING

GOD IS...

3 THINGS I'M THANKFUL FOR

THIS IS WHAT I LEARNED TODAY

TODAY I'M READING

GOD IS...

3 THINGS I'M THANKFUL FOR

THIS IS WHAT I LEARNED TODAY

TODAY I'M READING

GOD IS...

3 THINGS I'M THANKFUL FOR

THIS IS WHAT I LEARNED TODAY

TODAY I'M READING

GOD IS...

3 THINGS I'M THANKFUL FOR

THIS IS WHAT I LEARNED TODAY

TODAY I'M READING

GOD IS...

3 THINGS I'M THANKFUL FOR

THIS IS WHAT I LEARNED TODAY

TODAY I'M READING

GOD IS...

3 THINGS I'M THANKFUL FOR

THIS IS WHAT I LEARNED TODAY

TODAY I'M READING

GOD IS...

3 THINGS I'M THANKFUL FOR

THIS IS WHAT I LEARNED TODAY

TODAY I'M READING

GOD IS...

3 THINGS I'M THANKFUL FOR

THIS IS WHAT I LEARNED TODAY

TODAY I'M READING

GOD IS...

3 THINGS I'M THANKFUL FOR

THIS IS WHAT I LEARNED TODAY

TODAY I'M READING

GOD IS...

3 THINGS I'M THANKFUL FOR

THIS IS WHAT I LEARNED TODAY

TODAY I'M READING

GOD IS...

3 THINGS I'M THANKFUL FOR

THIS IS WHAT I LEARNED TODAY

TODAY I'M READING

GOD IS...

3 THINGS I'M THANKFUL FOR

THIS IS WHAT I LEARNED TODAY

TODAY I'M READING

GOD IS...

3 THINGS I'M THANKFUL FOR

THIS IS WHAT I LEARNED TODAY

TODAY I'M READING

GOD IS...

3 THINGS I'M THANKFUL FOR

THIS IS WHAT I LEARNED TODAY

TODAY I'M READING

GOD IS...

3 THINGS I'M THANKFUL FOR

THIS IS WHAT I LEARNED TODAY

TODAY I'M READING

GOD IS...

3 THINGS I'M THANKFUL FOR

THIS IS WHAT I LEARNED TODAY

TODAY I'M READING

GOD IS...

3 THINGS I'M THANKFUL FOR

THIS IS WHAT I LEARNED TODAY

TODAY I'M READING

GOD IS...

3 THINGS I'M THANKFUL FOR

THIS IS WHAT I LEARNED TODAY

TODAY I'M READING

GOD IS...

3 THINGS I'M THANKFUL FOR

THIS IS WHAT I LEARNED TODAY

TODAY I'M READING

GOD IS...

3 THINGS I'M THANKFUL FOR

THIS IS WHAT I LEARNED TODAY

TODAY I'M READING

GOD IS...

3 THINGS I'M THANKFUL FOR

THIS IS WHAT I LEARNED TODAY

TODAY I'M READING

GOD IS...

3 THINGS I'M THANKFUL FOR

THIS IS WHAT I LEARNED TODAY

TODAY I'M READING

GOD IS...

3 THINGS I'M THANKFUL FOR

THIS IS WHAT I LEARNED TODAY

TODAY I'M READING

GOD IS...

3 THINGS I'M THANKFUL FOR

THIS IS WHAT I LEARNED TODAY

TODAY I'M READING
_____
_____
_____
_____

GOD IS...
_____
_____
_____
_____

3 THINGS I'M THANKFUL FOR
_____
_____
_____

THIS IS WHAT I LEARNED TODAY
_____
_____
_____
_____
_____
_____
_____
_____
_____

TODAY I'M READING

_____
_____
_____
_____

GOD IS...

_____
_____
_____
_____

3 THINGS I'M THANKFUL FOR

_____
_____
_____

THIS IS WHAT I LEARNED TODAY

_____
_____
_____
_____
_____
_____
_____
_____
_____

TODAY I'M READING

GOD IS...

3 THINGS I'M THANKFUL FOR

THIS IS WHAT I LEARNED TODAY

TODAY I'M READING

GOD IS...

3 THINGS I'M THANKFUL FOR

THIS IS WHAT I LEARNED TODAY

TODAY I'M READING

GOD IS...

3 THINGS I'M THANKFUL FOR

THIS IS WHAT I LEARNED TODAY

TODAY I'M READING

GOD IS...

3 THINGS I'M THANKFUL FOR

THIS IS WHAT I LEARNED TODAY

TODAY I'M READING

GOD IS...

3 THINGS I'M THANKFUL FOR

THIS IS WHAT I LEARNED TODAY

TODAY I'M READING

GOD IS...

3 THINGS I'M THANKFUL FOR

THIS IS WHAT I LEARNED TODAY

TODAY I'M READING

GOD IS...

3 THINGS I'M THANKFUL FOR

THIS IS WHAT I LEARNED TODAY

TODAY I'M READING

GOD IS...

3 THINGS I'M THANKFUL FOR

THIS IS WHAT I LEARNED TODAY

TODAY I'M READING

GOD IS...

3 THINGS I'M THANKFUL FOR

THIS IS WHAT I LEARNED TODAY

TODAY I'M READING

GOD IS...

3 THINGS I'M THANKFUL FOR

THIS IS WHAT I LEARNED TODAY

TODAY I'M READING

GOD IS...

3 THINGS I'M THANKFUL FOR

THIS IS WHAT I LEARNED TODAY

TODAY I'M READING

GOD IS...

3 THINGS I'M THANKFUL FOR

THIS IS WHAT I LEARNED TODAY

TODAY I'M READING

GOD IS...

3 THINGS I'M THANKFUL FOR

THIS IS WHAT I LEARNED TODAY

TODAY I'M READING

GOD IS...

3 THINGS I'M THANKFUL FOR

THIS IS WHAT I LEARNED TODAY

TODAY I'M READING

GOD IS...

3 THINGS I'M THANKFUL FOR

THIS IS WHAT I LEARNED TODAY

TODAY I'M READING

GOD IS...

3 THINGS I'M THANKFUL FOR

THIS IS WHAT I LEARNED TODAY

TODAY I'M READING

GOD IS...

3 THINGS I'M THANKFUL FOR

THIS IS WHAT I LEARNED TODAY

TODAY I'M READING

GOD IS...

3 THINGS I'M THANKFUL FOR

THIS IS WHAT I LEARNED TODAY

TODAY I'M READING

GOD IS...

3 THINGS I'M THANKFUL FOR

THIS IS WHAT I LEARNED TODAY

TODAY I'M READING

GOD IS...

3 THINGS I'M THANKFUL FOR
marga thankful for

THIS IS WHAT I LEARNED TODAY

TODAY I'M READING

GOD IS...

3 THINGS I'M THANKFUL FOR

THIS IS WHAT I LEARNED TODAY

Though I cannot be near you now my family I trust. I trust in our creator God to always be between me and thee providing for your every need. May your holy angels be despatched to their every need, right when my babies need you. Right on time, never too late. Oh my God, giver of light and life I ask you now to grant my children favor. As well as my family members. All of them Lord. The ones I pray for every day. You know their needs before I ask. You know what each one will face on this earth. Convict each one of sin when needed Lord Jesus. Draw them to your cross and Holy Name. You are He who is faithful and True! I lift each one to you now by name and believe you to spare them and grant them eternal life! Help us to seek you, hear you, serve you, love you, God see if there is any wicked way in us and lead us in the way everlasting! The cry of my heart is to hear your voice as clearly as Adam & Eve before the fall! Make me bold as a lion, harmless as a lamb, wise as a serpent, harmless as a dove. Fulfill your purpose in me, in us oh God! Grant that we realize our destinies and purposes before we are too old to execute them! Perfect your perfect plan in us Lord while there's time and help me have peace while I wait and not panic! Never believe the lie that you aren't completing all God has for you to do if you are actively seeking His will, you are living His will. God takes every part of your life, even some wrong turns you've made, to complete His will in it. No fears. No worries. No regrets. Only Trust...